A Teddy Horsley Book

Music Makers

Teddy and Betsy make Music
Based on Psalm 150

by Leslie J Francis and Nicola M Slee
Pictures by Laur

G000294361

The Bear facts:

The Teddy Horsley Bible Series is designed to build bridges between the young child's day to day experiences of the world and major biblical themes and stories.

Both authors work in church-related institutions of education. Nicola Slee is currently Visiting Scholar at the Queen's College, Birmingham. Leslie Francis is Professor of Pastoral Theology at the University of Wales, Lampeter, and Trinity College, Carmarthen. The illustrator, Laura Cooper, is a teacher and artist.

The Teddy Horsley Series is a result of extensive research into the religious development of young children, and the authors' and illustrator's wide experience of educational work in schools and churches.

Published by:
National Christian Education Council
1020 Bristol Road
Selly Oak
Birmingham B29 6LB

British Library Cataloguing in Publication Data:
A catalogue record for this book is available from
the British Library.
Text © Leslie J Francis and Nicola M Slee 1990
Illustrations © Laura Cooper 1994

First published 1990
ISBN 0-7197-0841-9

Reprinted 1994, 1998
Printed in England

Teddy Horsley and Betsy Bear like to make music.

Together they prepare a special gift of music for Mr Henry's birthday.

Betsy Bear thumps Mrs Henry's piano,
but she can hardly reach the keys.

Teddy Horsley puffs into Mr Henry's trumpet, but he cannot make a note.

Betsy Bear blows Lucy's recorder,
but she hears only one shrill sound.

Teddy Horsley strums Walter's guitar,
but hurts his paw on the strings.

Betsy Bear shakes Lucy's tambourine,
but she catches Teddy's ear.

Teddy Horsley strikes Walter's chime bars, but he drops the hammer on his toes.

Betsy Bear clashes her cymbals
and laughs at the loud bright crash.

Teddy Horsley beats his drum
and dances at the strong deep boom.

They like to make music with cymbal and drum.
Crash, crash! Boom, boom!

Mr Henry is pleased with their gift of music.

Teddy Horsley and Betsy Bear bring their music to church with Mr and Mrs Henry, Lucy, and Walter.

Together they prepare a special gift for God on Sunday.

Mr Henry praises God
with the bright blast of the trumpet.

Mrs Henry praises God
with the rich sounds of the organ.

Walter praises God
with the clear chords of the guitar.

Lucy praises God
with the shrill notes of the recorder.

Betsy Bear praises God
with the loud crash of the cymbals.

Teddy Horsley praises God
with the deep boom of the drum.

They like to make music with cymbal and drum.
Crash, crash! Boom, boom!

The Lord is pleased with their gift of music.

The Teddy Horsley Bible Series is designed to build bridges between the young child's day to day experiences of the world and major biblical themes and stories.

In *Music Makers*, Teddy Horsley and Betsy Bear's experience of making music at home and in church brings alive the vision of praise in Psalm 150:

Praise the LORD!
Praise God in his Temple!
Praise his strength in heaven!
Praise him for the mighty things he has done.
Praise his supreme greatness.

Praise him with trumpets.
Praise him with harps and lyres.
Praise him with drums and dancing.
Praise him with harps and flutes.
Praise him with cymbals.
Praise him with loud cymbals.
Praise the Lord, all living creatures!

Praise the LORD!
Psalm 150. 1-6

The following questions suggest further ways of developing the links between the Bible passage and the young child's experience.

Talk about making music:
What music do you have in your house?
Who makes music in your house?
What can you make music with?
How many different kinds of sounds can you make?
What instruments have you tried playing?

Talk about the story:
What instruments did Betsy Bear try to play?
What instruments did Teddy Horsley try to play?
What problems did they have?
What instruments did Betsy and Teddy like best?
What sounds did they make?
Why did they prepare their music?
What instruments did Mr and Mrs Henry, Lucy, and Walter play?
Why did they prepare their music?

Titles in the *Teddy Horsley* series:

Autumn	*Do and Tell*	*Explorer*
Good Morning	*Hide and Seek*	*Lights*
Neighbours	*Night Time*	*The Grumpy Day*
The Picnic	*The Present*	*The Song*
The Sunny Morning	*The Walk*	*The Windy Day*
Water		

Hardback *Teddy Horsley* books:

LARGE format books with LARGE words and pictures, each containing three stories

Out and About with Teddy Horsley:
  ❖ *The Walk*
  ❖ *Explorer*
  ❖ *Neighbours*

A Day with Teddy Horsley:
  ❖ *Good Morning*
  ❖ *The Grumpy Day*
  ❖ *Night Time*

Teddy Horsley Activity Pack:
  ❖ One *Teddy Horsley* book
  ❖ *Teddy Horsley* activity book
  ❖ *Teddy Horsley* picture card
  ❖ *Teddy Horsley* cotton tidybag
  ❖ Crayons
  ❖ Removable stickers